The little ones are going on a big trip today. They've packed their bags and are ready to go. Have they got everything they'll need, do you think?

Goodbye, little house, see you soon! Where do you think the little ones will go to first?

suitcase   butterfly   sun hat   squirrel   umbrella

Yes, it's London, the capital city of the United Kingdom! London is a big, noisy city, full of cars, buses and grand buildings.

2

Drink tea!

Can you see...?

postbox

clock

taxi

policeman

Littleland

Around the World

Marion Billet

nosy crow

Hello and welcome to Littleland!

Can you see...?

map

camera

basket

rucksack

There's so much to see and do here. Just be careful when you cross the road, little ones!

phone box

teacup

Union Jack

postcard

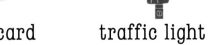
traffic light

The little ones' next stop is Paris, the capital of France. Can you say "Bonjour"? That means "Hello" in French. Can you see someone calling to their cat?

Can you see...?

croissant

cat

table

paintbrush

guitar   knickers   French flag   money   Eiffel Tower

This country is called Holland. It is famous for its pretty windmills and its colourful flowers. People often get to work and school by bicycle in Holland.

Can you see...?

tulip

barge

cheese

house

It's a windy day today! Hold on to your hats, little ones!

windmill   bicycle   Dutch flag   clogs   cow

The little ones are in a village, high up in the mountains of Germany now.

Can you see...?

castle

pretzel

pushchair

horn

There's a band playing in the main square. The little ones are having fun dancing to the merry tunes!

 accordion

 coin

 German flag

 sausage

 fountain

Finland is a very snowy country so it's the perfect place to go for a sleigh ride. What do you like to do in the snow?

Can you see...?

snowman

log

sleigh

carrot

Can you see someone in a red suit? Who do you think he is?

snowball   scarf   Finnish flag   mittens   reindeer

This is the beautiful city of Venice, in Italy. Here, they have canals instead of roads so people travel around in boats, not cars!

In Italy, people often eat pizza for their lunch. Do you like pizza, too?

Can you see...?

 ice cream

 pizza

duck

gondolier

ice cream

window   mask   Italian flag   gondola   pigeon

Do you know where this is? Yes, it's Egypt, home to the pyramids and an enormous statue called the Great Sphinx.

Can you see...?

camel · sunglasses · water bottle · Sphinx

What might the little ones take on a visit to the pyramids? Have they forgotten anything, do you think?

torch   donkey   Egyptian flag   rope   pyramid

The little ones are going on safari today.
They are in Kenya, a big country in Africa.

How many different
types of animal
can you see?

Can you
see...?

lion

pot

binoculars

giraffe

 antelope

 zebra

 Kenyan flag

 rhinoceros

 flamingo

Now the little ones are going to see a magnificent building called the Taj Mahal. They are in India, a very hot place indeed!

Can you see...?

 mangoes

 mat

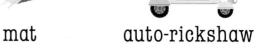 auto-rickshaw

 sitar

There are all sorts of ways of getting around in India – some people even travel by elephant!

bell   turban   Indian flag   elephant   pipe

The little ones have arrived in China now. They're just in time to join in with a festival!

Can you see...?

dragon   bird   drum   fan

The dragon is dancing to the music! How many people are inside the costume, do you think?

frog

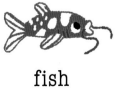
fish

Chinese flag

lily pad

lantern

It's night-time in Tokyo, the capital city of Japan. Just look at all those lights and signs!

しょくどう

Can you see...?

parasol   sushi roll   moon   robot

ぎんこう

すし

The little ones are enjoying exploring the streets and trying all sorts of exciting new things to eat.

teapot   tiger   Japanese flag   watermelon   rice

This is Australia, where the outback goes on for miles and miles and miles!

There aren't many people living here, but there are lots of interesting animals to spot!

Can you see...?

 kangaroo

 snake

koala

 aeroplane

windpump   sheep   Australian flag   boomerang   lizard

Hooray! It's time for some beach fun in sunny Brazil! Don't forget to put on your sunscreen, little ones!

Can you see...?

sandcastle   volleyball   rubber ring   bucket

Brazil!

Can you see something that you would like to be doing at the seaside?

goggles   shell   Brazilian flag   crab   flippers

The last country the little ones visit is the United States of America. They've come to busy New York City.

Can you see...?

baseball bat   apple   roller skates   bridge

What could be nicer than a picnic and some games in Central Park? It's a wonderful end to a great adventure!

The little ones' holiday is at an end and it's time to go back to Littleland. Bye-bye, New York. We're going home!

basketball   hot dog   American flag   banana   skyscraper

First published 2014 by Nosy Crow Ltd

The Crow's Nest, 10a Lant Street

London SE1 1QR

www.nosycrow.com

ISBN 978 0 85763 358 3

A CIP catalogue record for this book is available from the British Library.

Printed in China
Papers used by Nosy Crow are made from
wood grown in sustainable forests.

1 3 5 7 9 8 6 4 2